Developin
literacy
Skills

Through Science

KEY STAGE 2: Y3–4 P4–5

FRANCES MACKAY
PENNY VERNON
LINDA CORK

HOPSCOTCH
EDUCATIONAL PUBLISHING

◆ Contents ◆

◆ Introduction   3

◆ Teeth and eating   4

◆ Properties of materials   10

◆ Rocks and soils   16

◆ Magnets   22

◆ Light and shadows   28

◆ Habitats   34

◆ Keeping warm   40

◆ Solids and liquids   46

◆ Friction   52

◆ Circuits and conductors   58

Published by Hopscotch Educational Publishing Ltd,
Unit 2, 56 Pickwick Road, Corsham, Wiltshire. SN13 9BX
(Tel: 01249 701701)

© 2000 Hopscotch Educational Publishing

Written by Frances Mackay, Penny Vernon and Linda Cork
Series design by Blade Communications
Illustrated by Susan Hutchison
Cover illustration by Susan Hutchison
Printed by Clintplan, Southam

Frances Mackay, Penny Vernon and Linda Cork hereby assert
their moral right to be identified as the authors of this work in
accordance with the Copyright, Designs and Patents Act, 1988.

ISBN 1-902239-28-8

Introduction

 ## ABOUT THE SERIES

Developing Literacy Skills Through Science is a series of books aimed at developing key literacy skills using a range of written genres based on a science theme, from Key Stage 1 (P1–3) through to Key Stage 2 (P4–7).

The series offers a structured approach which provides detailed lesson plans to teach specific literacy and science skills. A unique feature of the series is the provision of differentiated photocopiable activities aimed at considerably reducing teacher preparation time. Suggestions for follow-up activities for both literacy and science ensure maximum use of this resource.

 ## ABOUT THIS BOOK

This book is for teachers of children at Key Stage 2, Years 3–4 and Scottish levels P4–5. It aims to:

◆ develop children's literacy and science skills through exposure to and experience of a wide range of stimulating texts with supporting differentiated activities which are both diversified and challenging;
◆ support teachers by providing practical teaching methods based on whole-class, group, paired and individual teaching;
◆ encourage enjoyment and curiosity as well as develop skills of interpretation and response.

 ## CHAPTER CONTENT

 ### Literacy objectives

These outline the aims for the literacy activities suggested in the lesson plan.

 ### Science objectives

These outline the science learning objectives that relate to the lesson plan.

 ### Resources

This lists the different resources that the teacher needs to teach the lesson.

 ### Starting point: Whole class

This provides ideas for introducing the activity and may include key questions to ask the children.

 ### Using the photocopiable text

This explains how to use the text extract provided with the children as a shared reading activity and introduction to the group work. It may also be used by groups during the group work.

 ### Group activities

This explains how to use each sheet as well as providing guidance on the type of child who will benefit most from each sheet.

 ### Plenary session

This suggests ideas for whole-class sessions to discuss the learning outcomes and follow-up work.

 ### Follow up ideas for literacy

This contains suggestions for further literacy activities related to the lesson plan which can be carried out at another time.

 ### Follow up ideas for science

This contains suggestions for further science activities which might be carried out at another time or during a designated science lesson.

Teeth and eating

Literacy objectives

+ To understand the difference between fact and opinion.
+ To locate information using headings, sub-headings and an index.

Science objectives

+ To understand that an adequate and healthy diet is needed to keep healthy.

Resources

+ Pictures of food groups: meat and fish, fats, sugars, starches, vegetables, fruit.
+ Books about healthy eating/diet/foods that contain headings, sub-headings and index pages.

Starting point: Whole class

+ Ask the children to tell you the types of foods they think they need to stay healthy. How do they know this? As we are growing up, how do we learn about the types and amounts of foods that we should eat to keep healthy? Talk about parental knowledge, information from doctors/ health centres, scientific advice and so on.
+ Show the children the pictures of the food groups and briefly agree the amount and types of foods that are required daily to keep healthy. Does it matter if there are some foods we never eat? Does everyone have to eat the same kinds of foods to stay healthy? (Consider vegans, vegetarians and different diets of different countries/religions.)
+ Show the children the books about healthy eating and explain that we can also learn about healthy eating by using information books and/or CD-Roms.
+ Look at the layout of the books and remind the children about the purpose of the contents and index pages. Share a page that has headings and sub-headings and discuss how they help us to locate information more quickly.

+ Finally, ask the children to tell you if they think the information contained in the books is fact or opinion. Ask them to consider statements such as 'Salad is horrible'. Is this fact or opinion? Discuss the difference.

Using the photocopiable text

+ Enlarge the text on page 6 on a photocopier or make enough copies for each child.
+ Share the text with the children. Is this piece of writing fiction or non-fiction? What makes them think so?
+ Look at the layout of the text – what devices are used to help us locate information more quickly? (Headings and sub-headings.)
+ Consider the facts and opinions in the text. Which are which? Ask the children to find at least two examples of both fact and opinion. Can the two ever be confused? Can facts 'change' over time? (James Lind believed his opinion to be scientific fact at the time.) Talk about how people's ideas in the past may seem ridiculous to us today because we now have such good communications and a wealth of scientific knowledge. Will the ideas we have today also change in the future?
+ Explain that the text has been taken from an information book that contains an index and that their task is to help compile this index. Look at the first paragraph again. Ask them to help you underline those words they think are key words and should be included in an index. Write these on the board and together put them in alphabetical order. Stress that they may need to look at the second and third letters of some words that begin with the same letter.

Group activities

Using the differentiated activity sheets

Activity sheet 1: This is aimed at children who need practice in ordering words alphabetically. They are given a list of words to insert into an index.

Teeth and eating

Activity sheet 2: This is aimed at children who have some experience of using an index. They are required to sort words using the 1st, 2nd and 3rd letters of words that begin with the same letter.

Activity sheet 3: This is aimed at more able children. They are required to write an index by sorting a list of words alphabetically.

 Plenary session

Bring the whole class together again when all the children have completed their activity sheets. Share their responses. Did they remember to look at the 2nd and 3rd letters of words to make sure they were in the correct order? Why do some words in the index have several page numbers? Compare the layout of this index with others in the information books. Are they similar? Do some use italics for the page numbers? Why?

 Follow up ideas for literacy

- Play a game to practise using an index. Each pair has an information book and they take it in turns to choose a word from the index for their partner to locate in the text.
- Prepare a set of questions for an information book that requires the children to use the index, contents, headings and sub-headings to find the answers.
- Ask the children to write lists of mixed facts and opinions and then give them to a partner to sort.

- Have a picture with a list of facts and opinions taken from it. Ask the children to sort the captions into 'fact', 'opinion' or 'cannot be sure'.
- Ask the children to use information books and/ or CD-Roms to find out more information about scurvy and other diseases that can be caused through a poor diet.
- Share food poems. Ask the children to write poems about healthy eating.
- Ask the children to write five questions they would like to find out the answers to in relation to page 6. They could find out the answers to their own or their partner's questions.

 Follow up ideas for science

- Find out about vitamins and investigate why we need different vitamins in our diet.
- Talk about the benefits of vitamins, protein and carbohydrates. Look at a child's typical lunch box – what is good in it and what isn't?
- By making a collection of food wrappers, investigate which foods contain vitamins.
- Ask the children to find out about other things that can affect our teeth and gums. Explain how to look after teeth correctly and the importance of healthy teeth.
- Discuss sweets and chocolates. Talk about chewing gum. At one time it was considered

bad for us but is now thought to be beneficial for the cleaning of teeth.
- Ask the children to find out about the purposes of different teeth such as molars and incisors. Compare them with the teeth of animals.
- Ask the children to use information books/ CD-Roms to find out about other scientists who have carried out research on deficiency diseases.
- Find out about animals that do not have teeth. How do they eat their food?
- Ask the children to keep a food diary for a week. They could graph the number of servings of particular foods, such as vegetables and fruit.

Scurvy

Scurvy is first recorded

In June 1497, Vasco Da Gama set out with four ships from Lisbon to sail around the southern cape of Africa to reach the rich Spice Islands of the Indies. When the ships had been at sea for about 12 weeks the men became ill. At first their gums grew large. Then their teeth became so loose that they rattled. The men could not eat and they developed sores on their bodies, which would not heal. They were close to death when a ship from the African port of Mombassa approached them and offered to guide them into port. The ship was loaded with fresh oranges, which the hungry men were able to suck. Soon they were all feeling better and Vasco Da Gama wrote in his diary, 'It pleased God in his mercy that all our sick recovered their health. It seems that the air of this place is very good.'

Medical theories

In those days it was a common theory of medicine that bad air carried diseases. This theory seemed to fit with scurvy. Since sailors always became ill after about 12 weeks at sea and were, therefore, a particular distance from shore, the scientists at that time thought that the air there must be bad.

In fact it was discovered that the sailors were suffering from a disease called scurvy. Nearly 300 years later scientists were still looking for an explanation for scurvy. James Lind, a Scottish naval doctor, carried out much research on scurvy. He found all sorts of cures but still no proper cause. He developed a theory that bad air blocked up the pores in the skin, preventing sweating. The blocked-in sweat went bad and caused scurvy and that when you ate oranges or lemons they mixed with the fat in your body to make a kind of soap which unblocked the pores and cured the sufferer.

Discovering the cause

Many more people, rich and poor, continued to suffer from scurvy and it wasn't until just before the First World War in 1913, that scientists published findings that seemed to suggest that you didn't catch scurvy by contact with anything; in fact you got it by **not** doing something. It was found that scurvy was a deficiency disease and was caused by a lack of vitamin C through not eating enough fresh fruit and vegetables.

Name _____

✦ Using an index ✦

✦ Below is part of the index page from the book that the text about scurvy was taken from. Some of the words in the text have been left out of the index. They are in the box. Decide where each word should go in the index and write it in.

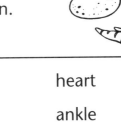

fats	germs	dentist	gums	heart
flour	diet	blood	Africa	ankle
apple	eggs	cheese	cereal	bread

Index

acne	12	calcium	6, 23	_____	16
ache	14, 24	_____	17, 37	fever	14, 33
_____	25, 36	_____	17	fibre	14
air	25	citrus fruit	17, 25	_____	13
_____	30				
_____	18	Da Gama	25	gargle	14
		dairy foods	17	_____	2, 33
		_____	14	_____	14, 25
baby teeth	14	_____	2, 15		
barley	19	disease	14, 25	health	2, 36
_____	5, 32			_____	7, 28
bones	6	_____	17	honey	13
_____	18	energy	15, 33	hospital	24, 33

Photocopiable

©Hopscotch Educational Publishing

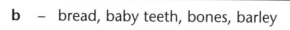

✦ Using an index ✦

✦ Below is part of the index page from the book that the text about scurvy was taken from. Some of the words in the text have been left out of the index. They are in the box. Sort them out and write them in the correct place in the index.

b –	bread, baby teeth, bones, barley
d –	disease, Da Gama, diet, dairy foods, dentist
f –	flour, fever, fibre, fats
h –	hospital, honey, health, heart

Index

acne	12	calcium	6, 23	_____	16
ache	14, 24	cereal	17, 37	_____	14, 33
Africa	25, 36	cheese	17	_____	14
air	25	citrus fruit	17, 25	_____	13
ankle	30				
apple	18				
		_____	25	gargle	14
		_____	17	germs	2, 33
_____	14	_____	14	gums	14, 25
_____	19	_____	2, 15		
_____	5, 32	_____	14, 25	_____	2, 36
_____	6			_____	7, 28
_____	18	eggs	17	_____	13
		energy	15, 33	_____	24, 33

✦ Using an index ✦

✦ Below is part of the index page from the book that the text about scurvy was taken from. Sort them into alphabetical order and set them out as an index. The numbers in brackets refer to the page numbers in the book.

> apple (18), energy (15, 33), gums (14, 25), germs (2, 33), health (2, 36), Da Gama (25), acne (12), cereal (17, 37), bread (18), eggs (17), flour (13), fever (14, 33), ankle (30), gargle (14), illness (2, 8), bones (6), fats (16), hospital (24, 33), calcium (6, 23), cheese (17), hygiene (2, 7), disease (14, 25), ache (14, 24), incisors (14), Indies (25), air (25), Africa (25, 36), honey (13), heart (7, 28), diet (2, 15), citrus fruit (17, 25), infection (22, 32), fibre (14), dairy foods (17), bread (18), iron (6), dentist (14), barley (19), baby teeth (14)

Index

Chapter 2

Properties of materials

 Literacy objectives

✦ To make a text into a chart by using information from the text.
✦ To infer meaning from text.

 Science objectives

✦ To develop knowledge and understanding of the different properties of materials.
✦ To use tables and charts to communicate data in an appropriate manner.

 Resources

✦ A collection of charts, such as a weekly weather chart or science results chart.

 Starting point: Whole class

✦ Ask the children if they have seen a game show. Write the names of some of them on the board (for example 'Family Fortunes').
✦ Are all the shows the same? What different formats are there? Agree some common factors, such as a host, some questions or tests of skill leading to a prize. Tell them that they are going to read a text about a game show and then work out the answers to the game show 'questions'.

 Using the photocopiable text

✦ Enlarge the text on page 14 on a photocopier or arrange for each pair of children to have a copy. Share the text with the children, either reading it out loud yourself or asking different children to read different parts of the text.
✦ How does the presenter make the game sound exciting? How could he have made it more exciting or more effective? (He didn't tell us what the star prize was!)
✦ Say that if Anna was allowed to make notes to help her, what format could she use that would be quick and easy to read? (A chart.) Show the

examples of charts to make sure the children understand how they can be set out and what they can be used for. Discuss how the game show information could be compiled into a chart. What kind of headings could she put in the chart?
✦ Draw up a chart, such as on the activity sheets, from the children's suggestions and model completing the chart for material number 1. You may need to define terms such as 'mineral', 'vegetable', transparent' and 'flexible'.
(The answer for number 1 is wood. Do not tell the children the answers to numbers 2 and 3, ie plastic and metal.)

 Group activities

Using the differentiated activity sheets

Activity sheet 1: This is aimed at children who are learning to extract information from text but are not confident at drawing up their own chart. They are asked to complete a pre-drawn chart using the information in the text about some materials. (Make sure the model is not visible.)

Activity sheet 2: This is aimed at children who are more confident at extracting information from text independently. They are given three new clues to different materials and asked to fill in a pre-drawn chart using the whole-class experience for support.(Answers: glass, wool, paper.)

Activity sheet 3: This is aimed at children who have already begun to draw their own charts. They are given clues to materials and are asked to construct a suitable chart for the information. (Answers: glass, wool, paper.)

Properties of materials

 Plenary session

♦ Bring the whole class together again when all the children have completed their activity sheets. Share the responses. Does everyone agree on the answers? Is it possible to have more than one correct answer per clue? Look at the charts drawn up by Group 3. Are they similar in any way?

♦ What other uses can the children suggest for drawing up charts? In what subject areas in school would they be most useful? Why? How do charts help us to understand a lot of information? Are they easier to read than a lot of text?

 Follow up ideas for literacy

♦ Continuing the idea of game shows, play Animal, Vegetable or Mineral type games and ask the children to focus on:
a) phrasing questions specifically
b) using precise vocabulary.

♦ Invent your own game show. Working in groups, pairs or individually, the children could invent and run an episode of their own game show. Consider the language used by the host to engage the interest of the audience. Discuss pace and how this makes a difference to the excitement of the game.

♦ Ask the children to use CD-Roms and/or information books to find out more information about different materials and their properties. The children could make a puzzle book with clues with lift-up flaps hiding the answers.

♦ Explore the clues hidden in riddles. Build up a collection of riddles and then challenge the children to write their own.

 Follow up ideas for science

♦ Look at materials and their properties. Do an investigation to find out the best wrapping paper for a parcel.
1) You will need lots of different samples of wrapping paper.
2) Ask the children what might happen to a parcel on its journey from the post box to the house of the person it is addressed to. (It will get rubbed, thrown around and possibly rained on.)
3) Using the selection of different papers, groups could test:
   – the ability to withstand wear (rubbing)
   – how waterproof the paper is
   – how strong it is (Hang weights onto a bulldog clip attached to the paper.)
   – how well it can be written on.

4) By combining results from all the experiments the class should be able to come to a conclusion about the best paper for the parcel.

♦ Investigate which material from a selection is the best for making a dishcloth to mop up spills.

♦ Consider properties of other materials and why they are used for specific purposes. For example, on a bicycle, why is the frame metal, but the tyres made from rubber and filled with air?

♦ Go on a 'material hunt' around the classroom or school. Ask the children to make a chart of objects they can find that are made from particular materials to find out which one is most commonly used. Discuss why this might be, relating to the properties of that material.

Ladies and gentlemen, good evening and welcome to tonight's round of **The Name's the Game** where you, the viewers, get the chance to identify people, places, objects and materials from a series of clues. There are super prizes waiting to be won.

Let's begin with our first contestant, Anna Clayphan. Your task tonight is to identify the three materials I will be describing, using the clues I will give you. Get all three right and tonight's star prize is yours!

Number 1

It is vegetable in origin. It will absorb water though not easily. It is never transparent and it is not usually flexible. It is hard and it doesn't conduct electricity.

Number 2

It is mineral in origin. It is waterproof and it can be transparent. It is usually flexible. It does not conduct electricity.

Number 3

It is mineral in origin and is waterproof. It is not transparent. It can sometimes be flexible and it is hard. Most kinds conduct electricity.

Are you ready Anna? You have two guesses for each material and your time starts NOW!

Name _____

✦ Using a chart ✦

✦ Complete the chart below using the information
you read in the game show text.

	origin	waterproof	transparent	flexible	hard	conducts electricity
Material number 1						
Material number 2						
Material number 3						

✦ Put a circle around the material you think is being described.

Material number 1   wood   grass

Material number 2   plastic   glass

Material number 3   metal   slate

13

✦ Using a chart ✦

✦ Here are some different clues for the game show. Use the information given in the clues to fill in the chart below.

Material A

It is mineral in origin. It is waterproof and transparent. It is not flexible, in fact it breaks easily. It is hard and will not conduct electricity.

Material B

It is animal in origin. It is waterproof and very flexible. It is not transparent and it does not conduct electricity. It is very soft.

Material C

It is vegetable in origin. It is not waterproof or transparent. It is very flexible. It will not conduct electricity.

Choice box
glass
metal
wool
leather
paper
wood
grass
stone

	origin	waterproof	transparent	flexible	hard	conducts electricity
Material A						
Material B						
Material C						

✦ Write here what you think the materials are. Select them from the Choice box.

Material A   _____

Material B   _____

Material C   _____

✦ Using a chart ✦

✦ Here are some different clues for the game show. Use the information given in the clues to draw chart and fill it in.

Material A
It is mineral in origin. It is waterproof and transparent. It is not flexible, in fact it breaks easily. It is hard and will not conduct electricity.

Material B
It is animal in origin. It is waterproof and very flexible. It is not transparent and it does not conduct electricity. It is very soft.

Material C

It is vegetable in origin. It is not waterproof or transparent. It is very flexible. It will not conduct electricity.

✎ Draw your chart here.

✦ Write here what you think the materials are.

Material A _____

Material B _____

Material C _____

Rocks and soils

 Literacy objectives

✦ To compare the way information is presented, for example by comparing a variety of information texts including ICT-based sources.
✦ To make a simple record of information from texts read.

 Science objectives

✦ To know that rocks are used for a variety of purposes.
✦ To know that rocks can be grouped according to observable characteristics.
✦ To know that rocks are chosen for particular purposes because of their characteristics.

 Resources

✦ A collection of different rocks, such as granite, conglomerate, sandstone and slate.

 Starting point: Whole class

✦ Tell the children that they are going to share a page that contains lots of information about rocks. What do they know already about rocks? Do they know the names of any? Do they know what rocks can be used for?
✦ If we wanted to find information about rocks where could we go, what could we use? Discuss the various possibilities, such as information books, encyclopaedias, CD-Roms, the Internet, rock societies/clubs and so on. Which source would they use first? Why? Which source do they think would be most up-to-date/correct? Why?
✦ Say that you want them to think about where the information might have come from when they look at the four different texts on the page they are about to share.

 Using the photocopiable text

✦ Enlarge the text (page 18) on a photocopier or provide each child with their own copy. Share the information contained in each text. Can they suggest where each one may have come from? (Information books, encyclopaedias or CD-Rom for 1–3 and the Internet for 4.)
✦ What information is each text giving us? Compare the differences in the ways the information is presented: 1 – text with headings, 2 – chart, 3 – labelled diagram and 4 – block text. Which type of presentation do the children prefer? Can they say why? Which type of presentation makes it easier for us to find information? Why? Compare text 1 with text 4. What does text 1 have that helps us find information? (Headings, words in bold.) Discuss how the chart in text 2 contains such a lot of information in a small space, without the need for sentences. Ask the children to tell you if they find illustrations/diagrams helpful in understanding something new. Why?
✦ Briefly discuss the importance of accuracy when finding information. How can we tell that a book is up-to-date? (Look at the date of publication.) Does it matter to us if the information has come from another country? (The website information is American.) Can facts change over time? (New discoveries are being made in science, for example, all the time.) Are all websites reliable? (Anyone can set up a website so they need to check several sites or use only recommended sites.) Explain that they need to keep these things in mind when they are finding out information about something.
✦ Finally, challenge the children to think of a way they could combine ALL the information from each of the four texts. (They could make a chart or they could continue the text as in text 1 by adding more headings to cover the information contained in texts 2, 3 and 4.) Tell them that they will be doing a similar task using an activity sheet.
✦ Share the rock collection. Can the children name some of the rocks using the information they have just read?

Rocks and soils

 Group activities

Using the differentiated activity sheets

Activity sheet 1: This is aimed at children who need support in making a list from a text.

Activity sheet 2: This is aimed at children who are capable of selecting the relevant facts from a text to include in a list.

Activity sheet 3: This is a more difficult text and is aimed at more able children.

 Plenary session

Share the children's responses to the activity sheets. How useful do they think lists are in summarising information? Do lists make it easy to find things? How else could the information have been presented? (As a chart?) What problems did they have when they were finding their own information? Did they have to use several sources? What form of presentation did they refer to? That is, did they use a chart? Diagrams? A page with headings?

 Follow up ideas for literacy

- ◆ Continue finding out about rocks. Make a class information book about them. Encourage the children to bring in rocks they have found to try and identify them.
- ◆ Share poems about rocks! For example, 'Stones' by Jean Kenward (*Earthways, Earthwise*, selected by Judith Nicholls, Oxford University Press).
- ◆ Because the information about rocks contains many technical words, ask the children to create a rock and soil dictionary or glossary.
- ◆ Challenge the children to find as many little words as they can in some of the longer, more difficult rock terms such as sedimentary (sediment, me, men, ta, tar, dim, dime).

- ◆ Ask the children to draw a flow diagram of a process to do with rocks, such as coal or slate mining/processing.
- ◆ Visit a mine. Ask the children to write a detailed description of what it might be like to be deep inside the earth. How would it make them feel? What would the surroundings be like?
- ◆ Explore the uses of rocks further. Ask the children to find out how steel is made, for example.
- ◆ Find out about all the rocks that are used in making a house. Draw and label a diagram.

 Follow up ideas for science

- ◆ Ask the children to group a collection of rock specimens according to their observable features, for example they could be grouped according to colour, texture or grain size. Challenge others to guess what criterion was used for the sorting.
- ◆ Ask the children to sort a collection of rocks and building materials into naturally occurring and those made by people, such as bricks or concrete.

- ◆ Ask the children to find out where soil comes from. How is it made?
- ◆ Take soil samples from different localities. What are the differences and similarities between them? Ask the children to record their observations in some way.

1

<u>What is a rock?</u>
Rocks are made up of minerals. Some are made of just one mineral but most are made of many minerals. Granite, for example, is made up of three minerals: quartz, feldspar and mica.

<u>What kinds of rock are there?</u>
There are hundreds of different kinds of rocks but there are three main types of rock: **igneous**, **sedimentary** and **metamorphic**.

2

rock	colour	minerals	use
granite	red, pink, yellow, brown	quartz, feldspar, mica	buildings, roads
slate	grey, black, green, red	quartz, muscovite	roofs, floors
sandstone	red, grey, brown	quartz	buildings
marble	many	calcite	floors, work surfaces, sculptures
pumice	buff, grey	glass	polish, building materials, scouring

3

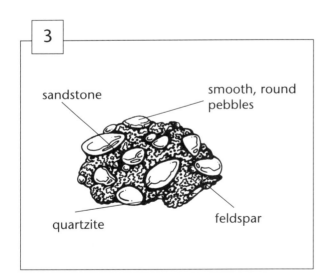

sandstone — smooth, round pebbles — quartzite — feldspar

4

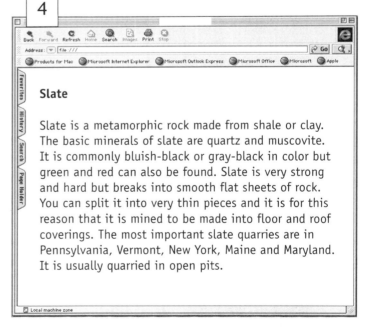

Slate

Slate is a metamorphic rock made from shale or clay. The basic minerals of slate are quartz and muscovite. It is commonly bluish-black or gray-black in color but green and red can also be found. Slate is very strong and hard but breaks into smooth flat sheets of rock. You can split it into very thin pieces and it is for this reason that it is mined to be made into floor and roof coverings. The most important slate quarries are in Pennsylvania, Vermont, New York, Maine and Maryland. It is usually quarried in open pits.

✦ Rocks ✦

✦ Read the following information about different kinds of rocks. Use the <u>underlined</u> words to make a list of the main features about each one. The first one has been done for you.

<u>Basalt</u> can be <u>black</u>, <u>dark grey</u> or <u>dark green</u> in colour. Basalt is <u>hard</u> to scratch with a fingernail. It is fairly <u>smooth</u>. Basalt can be crushed and sold to make many useful things. It is used in pavements, roads and buildings.

<u>Limestone</u> can be <u>black</u>, <u>grey</u>, <u>white</u> or <u>tan</u>. The rock is fairly <u>soft</u>. Fossil limestone has the fossils of shells and animals in it. It can be <u>rough</u> or <u>smooth</u>. It can be used as a building stone and in making cement.

<u>Quartzite</u> is a <u>pale white</u> colour. It can be <u>smooth</u>. It is <u>very hard</u>.

<u>Obsidian</u> is <u>like coloured glass</u>. It is very <u>smooth</u> and <u>hard</u>. It can be <u>many colours</u>.

<u>Basalt</u> black, dark grey, dark green hard smooth	

✦ Now use some information books or a CD-Rom to find some information about another rock. Make a list of its features.

✦ Rocks ✦

✦ Read the following information about different kinds of
rocks. In the chart below, list the main features about
each one. The first one has been done for you.

Basalt is a rock that comes from volcanoes. It is an igneous rock. It can be black,
dark grey or dark green in colour. It is made up of feldspar and olivine minerals.
Basalt is hard to scratch with a fingernail. It is fairly smooth. Basalt can be crushed
and sold to make many useful things. It is used in pavements, roads and buildings.

Limestone is a sedimentary rock. It can be black, grey, white or tan. It is made up of
calcite minerals. The rock is fairly soft. Fossil limestone has the fossils of shells and
animals in it. It can be rough or smooth. It can be used as a building stone and in
making cement.

Quartzite is a metamorphic rock. It is a pale white colour. It can be smooth. It
contains quartz minerals. It is very hard.

Obsidian is an igneous rock. It looks like coloured glass and can be found in many
colours. It is very smooth and hard. In times gone by people used it to make arrow
and spear heads.

<u>Basalt</u> igneous black, dark grey, dark green feldspar and olivine minerals hard smooth	

✦ Now use some information books or a CD-Rom to find out some
information about another rock. Make a list of its features.

✦ Rocks ✦

✦ Read the following information about different kinds of rocks. List the main features of each one that would help you identify it.

Basalt is the most common type of volcanic rock. It is therefore igneous. It is usually dark grey but can be black or dark green in colour. It is made up of fine- grained minerals such as feldspar and olivine. Basalt is hard to scratch with a fingernail. It is fairly smooth. Basalt can be crushed and sold to make many useful things. It is used in pavements, roads and buildings.

Limestone is a sedimentary rock. It can be black, grey, white or tan. It is made up of calcite minerals. The rock is fairly soft. Fossil limestone has the fossils of shells and animals in it. It can be rough or smooth. It can be used as a building stone and in making cement. Lime can also be made when it is heated. Chalk is a variety of limestone.

Quartzite is a metamorphic rock. It is a pale white colour. It can be smooth. It is mainly composed of quartz but can contain small amounts of mica, nutile, feldspar, tourmaline and zircon minerals. It is very hard.

Obsidian is volcanic glass and is an igneous rock. It is semi-translucent and looks like coloured glass. It is usually black but can be found in many colours. It is very smooth and hard. In times gone by people used it to make arrow and spear heads.

✦ Write your lists here:

[blank box]

✦ Now use some information books or a CD-Rom to find out some information about another rock. Make a list of its features.

Magnets

 ## Literacy objectives

- To consider how written instructions are organised, for example lists, numbered points, diagrams with arrows, bullet points.
- To write instructions using a range of organisational devices, recognising the importance of correct sequence.

 ## Science objectives

- To understand that the behaviour of magnets can be investigated.

 ## Resources

- A collection of different sets of instructions, for example instructions for games, classroom activities and construction kits.

 ## Starting point: Whole class

- Tell the children that they are going to look at some instructions today. Have they used some instructions themselves recently? To do what? Could they follow the instructions easily? Where might they find instructions? (On games, for making things, recipes and so on.) How are instructions different from other forms of writing, such as stories and information books?
- Show the children the samples of instructions. Discuss the purpose of each one and how they are set out. Point out the organisational devices such as lists, dashes, commas for lists in sentences, bullet points and labelled diagrams. Talk about the usefulness of each of these devices.
- Now ask the children to follow some simple oral instructions that you give them. (Make up two sets of instructions – one that is sequential and one that is not.) Can the children tell you the differences between the two sets of instructions? How important is it to follow instructions in the correct order? Do all instructions have to be followed in a particular order?

- Explain that they are now going to read a set of instructions for an experiment. Ask them to look out for the instructional devices you have already discussed.

 ## Using the photocopiable text

- Enlarge the text on page 24 on a photocopier or arrange for each pair of children to have a copy. Read the text with the children, either reading it out loud yourself or asking different children to read different parts of the text.
- What are the instructions about? How are they organised? How does the setting out of the instructions help us to follow them in order? Are the diagrams helpful? Why?
- What kind of language is used? What kind of word tends to be the first word in an instruction? (verb) The text uses the term 'e.g.' What does this mean?
- Do they consider the instructions to be well set out? Could it be improved in any way?
- Do they think they could follow these instructions to do the experiment themselves?

 ## Group activities

Using the differentiated activity sheets

Activity sheet 1: This is aimed at children who need a lot of support when writing instructions. They are given a writing frame and are asked to complete the instructions by filling in the missing words.

Activity sheet 2: This is aimed at children who have more experience at writing instructions. They are required to write the instructions with only the diagrams as clues.

Activity sheet 3: This is aimed at more able children who are confident enough to write a set of instructions from an account of an experiment.

Chapter 4

Magnets

 Plenary session

✦ Share the results from the activity sheets. How important were the diagrams in aiding Groups 1 and 2 to complete their instructions? Do the instructions written by Group 3 differ? In what ways? How similar are their diagrams to those in Groups 1 and 2?

✦ Could the instructions for all three groups be improved in any way? Are they confident that someone could use these instructions to successfully repeat the experiment?

 Follow up ideas for literacy

✦ Ask the children to write sets of instructions for games played in the classroom, playground or PE lessons. Can others follow them to successfully play the game?

✦ Ask them to write a set of instructions of a game for younger children. What things do they need to consider? How important will illustrations/diagrams be? How might the language they use change?

✦ Ask the children to bring in samples of instructions from home. Make a class display.

Use the display as a stimulus for further discussion – Which instructions are the worst? Why? Which instructions are best? Why?

✦ Share recipes. Ask the children to write a recipe for a simple task, such as making a peanut butter sandwich. Ask them to think carefully about each step. Have they left out anything important?

✦ Write stories that use instructions, for example a treasure hunt.

 Follow up ideas for science

✦ Carry out the two experiments in the lesson. Ask the children to consider if the tests are fair. How could they improve the tests? Could they add a wider choice of materials, for example. Ask them to explain what the results of their investigations show us.

✦ Ask the children to use information books and CD-Roms/the Internet to find out how magnets are used in our everyday lives. Make a class display of their findings.

✦ Explore the forces of attraction and repulsion between magnets. Ask the children to record what happens when magnets are put together.

✦ Extend the investigation about the attraction of magnets through materials by finding out whether the thickness of the material has any effect on the strength of attraction. You could use pieces of card of the same thickness, for example, and find out how many pieces of card it takes before the magnet stops attracting the paper clip through it.

✦ Do magnets attract all metals? Provide a wide selection of metals, such as coins, brass weights, copper wire, spoons and tin plate lids. (Note: Only iron, nickel and cobalt are attracted, but some alloys, such as steel, are also magnetic.)

How to find the strongest magnet

You will need:

several different sized magnets of different shapes, for example bar and horseshoe, paper clips, paper, pencil

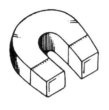 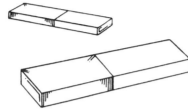 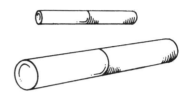

What to do:

● Choose a magnet.

● Get the paper clips and hang them from the magnet one at a time to make a chain.

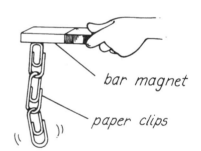

bar magnet

paper clips

● Keep adding the paper clips until the chain of clips falls off.

● Count how many paper clips were held in the chain.

● Record your answer in a table.

type of magnet	how many paper clips it held
small bar	8
big bar	12
small horseshoe	6

Activity 1

◆ Magnets ◆

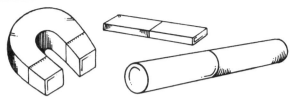

◆ Complete the instructions below by using the diagrams to help you.

How to find out if a magnet will work through different materials

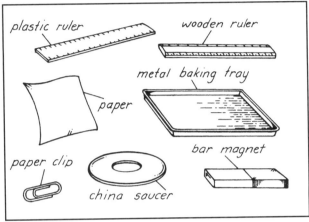

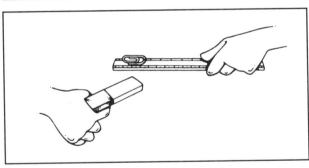

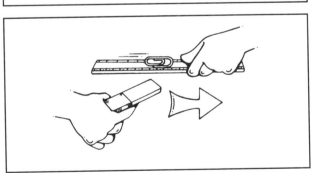

material	will the magnet work through it?
wood	yes
plastic	
metal	
china	
paper	

You will need:

a bar _____

paper _____

a _____ ruler

a plastic _____

a metal baking _____

a china _____

What to do:

1. Place a _____ clip on top of the wooden _____.

2. Hold a bar _____ underneath the ruler.

3. Move the magnet underneath the _____. Watch what happens to the _____ clip on top.

4. Record whether or not the paper clip _____.

5. Repeat this test with all the other _____.

◆ Magnets ◆

◆ Write the instructions for the experiment below by using the diagrams to help you. Remember to keep your instructions clear and precise.

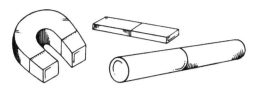

How to find out if a magnet will work through different materials

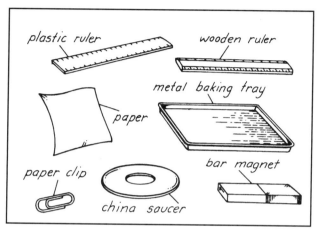

plastic ruler   wooden ruler

paper   metal baking tray

paper clip   china saucer   bar magnet

You will need:

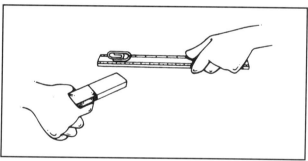

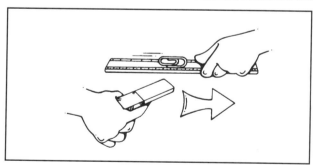

What to do:

material	will the magnet work through it?
wood plastic metal china paper	yes

Photocopiable

◆ Magnets ◆

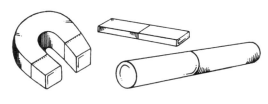

◆ Read the science report below. Use the information in the report to write and draw a set of instructions for the experiment. Remember to make your instructions clear and precise so that someone else could use them to repeat the experiment.

Our Science Report: Does A Magnet Work Through Different Materials?

We got a bar magnet and a paper clip. Then we made a collection of different materials: a wooden ruler, a plastic ruler, a metal baking tray, a china saucer and a piece of paper. We put the paper clip on top of the wooden ruler. Then we held the magnet underneath it. We moved the magnet and watched what happened to the paper clip. If it moved, we knew that the magnet worked through the wood. We recorded what happened in a table. We repeated this with all the other materials and recorded what happened.

◆ Write your instructions here. Draw diagrams to illustrate the instructions.

Light and shadows

 Literacy objectives

+ To use dictionaries to check the definitions of words.
+ To write own definitions of words.
+ To locate information using a glossary.

 Science objectives

+ To know that opaque materials do not let light through and transparent materials let a lot of light through.
+ To know that some objects reflect light.
+ To know that shadows change in length and position throughout the day.

 Resources

+ Some information books about light and shadows that contain a contents, index and glossary page.
+ Dictionaries.
+ Some objects/materials that are opaque, transparent and translucent.

 Starting point: Whole class

+ Tell the children that they are going to share a story about some children who go to a fair. Explain that while at the fair they notice three unusual things. Ask them to work out what these three things are as you read the story.

 Using the photocopiable text

+ Enlarge the text on page 30 on a photocopier or arrange for each pair of children to have a copy. Share the text with the children, either reading it out loud yourself or asking different children to read different parts of the text.
+ What were the three unusual things the children noticed at the fair? (Transparent/translucent glass, different reflections in mirrors, changing length and position of shadows.)

+ Have the children any experience of these things themselves? Have they been to a Hall of Mirrors? What did they notice? Have they noticed how their shadow changes? Have they ever looked at things through frosted glass?
+ Ask them to tell you how they think Ashia might find out why these things happen? Show them the collection of books about light and shadows. If Ashia was to use these where might she look first? Select one of the books. Remind the children about using a contents and index page. Look at the chapter headings and discuss how Ashia might decide which chapter(s) to look in.
+ Choose a chapter which contains some specialist vocabulary. Select one or two words and invite the children to define them. Write up their definitions. (Use the term 'definition'.) Then look the words up in a dictionary. How did their meanings compare with the dictionary meaning? Discuss how writers of non-fiction books often use a glossary to explain specialist vocabulary. Share the glossary in the book.
+ Refer back to the text. Are there any specialist words used here that the children may want to find out the meaning of? Underline 'transparent' and 'reflection' for example. Look up the meanings of these words in a dictionary. (You may like to briefly show the children the collection of things that are transparent, translucent and opaque to help them understand the meaning of the terms.)
+ Tell them that they are now going to help Ashia find out the meaning of some of the words she did not understand in her book about light and shadows.

 Group activities

Using the differentiated activity sheets

Activity sheet 1: This is aimed at children who need practice in using a dictionary. They are required to match words with dictionary definitions.

Light and shadows

Activity sheet 2: This is aimed at children who are more confident in using a dictionary. They are required to write definitions for a list of words.

Activity sheet 3: This is aimed at more able children. They are required to identify technical words in a passage and to write a definition of these words as they would appear in a glossary.

 Plenary session

◆ Share the responses to the activity sheets. Are they agreed on the definitions? What do you need to do if you do not understand the definition given in a dictionary? (Try a different dictionary, look up unknown words in the definition.) Did the children in Group 3 underline the same words? Can they justify their choices? If possible, look at the glossary entries for some of the words in the collection of books to compare them.

 Follow up ideas for literacy

◆ Use the words from the text to begin a class science dictionary. Add to the dictionary throughout the year.

◆ Practise using a thesaurus to find other words that mean the same as some of the words in the text, such as transparent. Explore synonyms of other words.

◆ Read poems about shadows, such as 'My Shadow' by Robert Louis Stevenson. Ask the children to write their own shadow poems.

◆ Ask the children to write a story centred around the Hall of Mirrors – perhaps a magic mirror or a mirror that causes people to stay looking like their reflection!

◆ Challenge the children to use CD-Roms and/or information books to find out more about light, mirrors and/or shadows.

◆ Use safety mirrors and ask the children to write a detailed description of themselves!

 Follow up ideas for science

◆ To explore the terms 'transparent', 'translucent' and 'opaque', investigate which things create dark shadows, light shadows and no shadows at all.

◆ Do an investigation with a shadow stick. Go out at different times of the day and mark the shadow. Do this during the summer and the winter. Spot the differences in length and position of the shadows. Can the children think why they might be different?

◆ Use a light source such as an overhead projector. Provide the children with a regular shaped opaque object. Ask them to investigate what happens to the size of the shadow as the distance from the light source varies. Can they think of a way to measure this?

◆ Ask the children to observe their shadows outside on a sunny day. Ask them to stand, sit and crouch in different positions. What happens to their shadow?

◆ Using two safety mirrors, ask the children to explore what happens when the mirrors are placed at different angles to each other. What happens to the reflection?

◆ Make periscopes from empty milk cartons. How do they work?

◆ Using a collection of different materials, shine a torch on them in a darkened room. Which materials give the best reflection? Try smooth and crumpled aluminium foil. Which one reflects best? Why?

The Fair

Ashia and her little brother were visiting the local fair. He hadn't been before and was beside himself with excitement at all the magical coloured lights and fantastic rides.

"Look!" he cried, pointing to a stall selling stained-glass mobiles and mirrors. "Aren't they lovely? Do you think Mum would like one?"

Ashia looked closely at the beautiful coloured glass and noticed that some of the glass was transparent and she could see right through them. But she also noticed that everything looked quite blurry through the frosted glass.

"Yes," she said. "They are lovely, but I don't think we can afford one."

Next thing she knew, Ashia was being dragged towards the Hall of Mirrors.

"Oh look at us!" screamed her brother. "Look at how tall and skinny we look!" Ashia began to giggle as she looked at her reflection in the different mirrors. At one mirror she looked really short and fat with tiny little legs and at the next her head looked enormous on a little body. There was even a mirror that made them look upside down.

"How is it done?" asked her brother.

"I don't really know," said Ashia. But she noticed that the mirrors themselves were all different shapes. Perhaps that had something to do with it.

On the way home, Ashia's brother noticed something else interesting. "Look!" he said. "My shadow's moved. It's around the other side of me now. I'm sure it wasn't there when we came to the fair. And it's changed shape! It's got longer! Just like when we were in the Hall of Mirrors!"

All the way home Ashia thought about all the things she and her brother had noticed at the fair. She knew there was a book in her bedroom all about light and shadows. So she decided that she would try and find out more.

◆ Definitions ◆

◆ Here are the words that Ashia looked up in her book about light and shadows. Unfortunately, the meanings for each word have got mixed up! Use a dictionary to look up the meanings of the words. Then draw a line from each word to its meaning. One has been done for you.

transparent	not clear, hazy or indistinct
mirror	anything that illuminates, such as a lamp, candle or the Sun
reflect	allows light to pass through, clear enough to see through
shadow	a glass or metal surface that reflects an image of something placed in front of it
light	allows light to pass through but things look blurry if you look through it
opaque	to throw back light, heat or sound
translucent	a dark shape on a surface caused when something is between a light and the surface
blurry	does not allow light to pass through

◆ Now use your dictionary to look up the meaning of reflector. Write a definition here:

◆ Definitions ◆

◆ When Ashia read her book about light and shadows, she came across a lot of words she did not understand. They are listed below. Use a dictionary to write a definition of each one.

transparent   _____

_____

translucent   _____

_____

opaque   _____

_____

reflect   _____

_____

shadow   _____

_____

illuminate   _____

_____

concave   _____

_____

convex   _____

_____

◆ Now look at the words again. Decide which ones you think should go in a glossary at the back of the book. Put a circle around them.

✦ Definitions ✦

✦ Below is part of a passage from Ashia's book about light and shadows. <u>Underline</u> ten words that you think should go in a glossary at the back of the book.

Transparent things let light go straight through them. Translucent things let light through but they scatter the light. Things look blurry if you look through these materials. Opaque things do not let any light through. When light hits an opaque object, a dark area forms behind the object. This is called a shadow.

The shape of a reflection in a mirror depends upon the shape of the mirror. If it is concave, then the effect is to make something smaller than it really is, whereas a convex mirror enlarges the reflection.

✦ Now list the underlined words and use a dictionary to look up their meanings. Record their meanings in the glossary below:

Glossary

Habitats

 ## Literacy objectives

♦ To discuss the purpose and format of different types of letters.
♦ To write a letter for a specific purpose.
♦ To organise a letter into simple paragraphs.

 ## Science objectives

♦ To recognise ways in which living things and the environment need protection.

 ## Resources

♦ Some samples of different types of letters – personal, business and letters to a newspaper.

 ## Starting point: Whole class

♦ Tell the children that they are going to look at some extracts from letters. What does 'extract' mean? Tell them that one of the extracts is from a letter written to a local newspaper. What sorts of things do people write to the newspaper about? Share an example from your sample. Does everyone agree with the content of such letters? Who might have the opposite view to the writer of this letter?
♦ What other kinds of letters are there? List them on the board. Tell the children that you want them to tell you what kind of letter the other extracts are after they've read them.

Using the photocopiable text

♦ Enlarge the text on page 36 on a photocopier or arrange for each pair of children to have a copy. Share the four extracts. How can we tell they are all letters? Which extract is the letter written to the newspaper? How can they tell? What kind of letters are the other extracts? Is the language and tone used in these the same as the newspaper one? Why would there be a difference? Who do you think Amy is writing to? What do you think the replies to Amy's letters contained? What tells you this? What do you think Amy's friend's last idea is going to be? What would you do if you were in this situation?
♦ Explain that they are going to write a letter to the council, pretending they are Amy. Discuss how business letters are set out and how they begin and end. Share letters from your sample collection.
♦ Look at how the sample letters are set out in paragraphs and how each paragraph has a main topic/idea/purpose. Copy the letter out on the board to model how it is written and set out.

 ## Group activities

Using the differentiated activity sheets

Activity sheet 1: This is aimed at children who need help with writing a letter. They are provided with a letter already set out and are required to complete it using a word box to help them.

Activity sheet 2: This is aimed at children who have more experience of letter writing. They are given help in setting out the paragraphs but still need to write the body of the letter themselves.

Activity sheet 3: This is aimed at more able children. They are required to write the letter without any guidance on how to set out the page.

Habitats

 ## Plenary session

♦ Share some of the children's letters. Do they conform to a more formal business style? Do they begin and end in a business-like way? Do the children think they have made their point clear to Mr Casey? Do they think their letter will convince him to do something about it?

♦ Look at the content of the paragraphs in the letters. Is each one concerned with a different subject/point? Have the children in group 3 set the addresses out correctly? How does the setting out differ from a personal letter?

 ## Follow up ideas for literacy

♦ Ask the children to write a follow-up letter to Amy's friend, telling about the letter she wrote to the council and what happened as a result.

♦ Ask the children to cut out letters about local issues from their newspapers. Build up a class collection. Write a 'real' letter in response to an issue that especially concerns the children.

♦ Ask the children to design an advertising campaign to keep the park clean and tidy and the wildlife safe. They could produce posters, leaflets, radio jingles and so on.

♦ Write letters to another class in the school or a different school to ensure their letter writing has a real purpose. Send e-mails to another class in another school. (There are certain e-mail packages, such as Excitepost, that prevent children receiving messages from anyone not in their address book. As with other forms of letter writing, always closely supervise the messages the children send.)

 ## Follow up ideas for science

♦ Go pond dipping in a local pond. Make sure you talk to the children about a 'country code' beforehand and make sure you have adequate adult supervision. Keep animal specimens in the shade to prevent overheating and return them to the pond as soon as possible.

♦ Compare the wildlife of the pond with another habitat, such as a field or wood. What are the differences and similarities between the things that live there? How are they adapted to their environment?

♦ Ask the children to use CD-Roms to find out more information about pond creatures.

♦ Discuss ways in which different habitats can be protected and why this is necessary.

♦ Find out about animals/ plants that are in danger of extinction. Find out what can be done to help them.

♦ Investigate food chains. Discuss how pollution can kill off one section of the chain and therefore affect everything else in the chain.

♦ Use identification keys to identify local plants and animals.

♦ Provide the children with a collection of pictures of animals and plants of local and foreign species. Ask them to sort the collection in different ways, such as 'Things that would live in our local area and things that would not'; 'Things that belong together' (need to justify why) or 'Things that would live on land and things that would live in water' (say why).

A

…why something can't be done about it, I'll never know. It's about time the council spent some of its money on things that really matter to the local residents instead of spending it on things such as that expensive statue that was put up in Market Square last month. What we need is a nice clean park that is safe for people AND wildlife!

Mrs R Thomas, Bingley Square

B

So as I said, it's really quiet here without you living next door. Seriously, I hope you like your new school and I'm sure you'll make lots of new friends. I haven't been to the park since you left so I can't tell you any news about the frogs! Must go, keep in touch,

Love Amy

C

…You'll never guess what's happened at the park! I went there yesterday and you'll never believe this – there was rubble and junk everywhere! People think that a local builder has been dumping his rubbish there. But the worst thing is, the pond's covered too! So I haven't seen our frogs – I hope they're all right. What should I do? Write soon,

Love Amy

D

….and Mrs Bingley's even written to the paper! Thanks for your idea about a petition. I've already got 20 names on it, but I'm really worried that it might be too late for the frogs. Have you got any other ideas? Write back VERY soon,

Love Amy

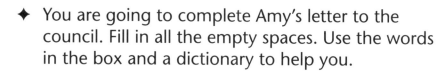 

✦ You are going to complete Amy's letter to the council. Fill in all the empty spaces. Use the words in the box and a dictionary to help you.

sincerely	wildlife	danger	destroyed	harm	die
concerned	local		anything	safe	rubbish

Mr John Casey
Council Offices
Town Hall
Wellington
WL11 4EP

7 Windsor St
Parklane
Wellington
WL10 9EX

_____ 2 _____

Dear _____

My name is _____. I am writing to you because I am

very worried about _____.

For years I have been watching the frogs in the pond and I do not want

_____.

My friend, _____, has suggested I get a petition together. I am

sending it with this letter. I have got _____ to sign it. This shows that

lots of people _____.

Please can you _____

_____.

Yours _____

Amy Willow

Activity 2

Name _____

✦ Letter to the council ✦

✦ You are going to write Amy's letter to the council. Write your letter using 3 paragraphs. Write about the following things in these paragraphs:

1. Introduce yourself and say why you are writing, what you are worried about.

2. Mention the petition you have got together.

3. Ask the councillor for his help.

Mr John Casey
Council Offices
Town Hall
Wellington
WL11 4EP

7 Windsor St
Parklane
Wellington
WL10 9EX

_____ 2 _____

Dear _____

Yours _____

Amy Willow

Literacy through science
KS2 Y3–4/P4–5

Photocopiable

©Hopscotch Educational Publishing

Activity 3

◆ Letter to the council ◆

◆ You are going to write Amy's letter to the council. You are going to write to Mr John Casey. Tell him why you are writing and what you are worried about. Tell him about your petition. Ask him how he is going to solve the problem. Remember to set out your letter in paragraphs.

Keeping warm

 ## Literacy objectives

+ To develop rules for good report writing.
+ To write a report using organisational devices, for example numbered lists and headings, by generalising some of the details and deleting the least important details.

 ## Science objectives

+ To understand that good thermal insulators keep cold objects cold and warm objects warm.

 ## Resources

+ A collection of reports, such as a sports match report or a visiting governor's report.

 ## Starting point: Whole class

+ Ask the children to tell you what they think a report is. What kinds of reports do they know of? (School report, science report.)
+ Share some of the reports from the collection. What things do they have in common? Do they just contain facts? Are there different styles depending on who is supposed to read them?
+ Tell them that you want them to think about what makes a good report by looking at some more examples written by children.

 ## Using the photocopiable text

+ Enlarge the text on page 42 on a photocopier or arrange for each pair of children to have a copy. Share the texts with the children.
+ Ask them to comment on the report's usefulness/ effectiveness after they have read it. Analyse each one, looking for ways it could be improved. Focus on text 3. What makes this a successful report?

Note the use of impersonal style, use of passive voice, no unnecessary detail, clear and concise sentences, chronological order, use of headings and numbering.
+ Ask the children to think of some rules for 'good' report writing. Agree them and list them on the board.
+ Explain that they are now going to put these rules to use by improving another child's science report.

 ## Group activities

Using the differentiated activity sheets

Activity sheet 1: This is aimed at children who need support in setting out and wording a report.

Activity sheet 2: This is aimed at children who have some experience of report writing but still need a supportive framework.

Activity sheet 3: This is aimed at more able children who can select the main ideas for report writing and are capable of setting out the report themselves.

Keeping warm

 Plenary session

◆ Share Rebekah's original report together. Do the children agree which sentences are not necessary and why? Share some of the children's re-written reports. Have they included all the important information? Did they remember to write clearly without unnecessary detail? Did they present the report in chronological order?

◆ Compare the reports written by Group 3. What organisational devices did they use to set out their reports clearly and concisely? Did they use headings or numbering? Do the children think that this activity will help them when they come to writing a science report of their own? How?

 Follow up ideas for literacy

◆ Look for opportunities for the children to put their report writing skills into practice. Ask them to write reports for a school assembly, the school notice board or a newsletter about a school trip, play or guest speaker.

◆ Challenge them to write their own school report! How truthful are they prepared to be?

◆ Explore the theme of keeping warm. Share some poems about the winter's cold, such as 'Winter Morning' by Ogden Nash (*I Like This Poem*, edited by Kaye Webb, Puffin) and then challenge the children to find and/or write some poems that would warm them up!

◆ Use a report you have prepared yourself, for example about a lost tribe or a hidden city to act as a stimulus for creative writing.

◆ Ask the children to prepare a poster about how to stay warm in winter. Encourage them to use information sources to find out factual information and to translate this into helpful diagrams and text. For example a labelled diagram of suggested winter clothing.

 Follow up ideas for science

◆ Practise measuring temperature with a thermometer. Give the children a selection of different temperatures of water and ask them to put them in order by temperature. What happens if they take too long doing this task?

◆ Collect a sample of different take-away food packaging. Ask the children to test out the hot potato experiment themselves. Ask them to record their results. Does everyone have the same result? Why do they think different types of foods are packaged in different types of containers? (flat pizza boxes, plastic Chinese take-away cartons, fish and chip paper). Can they suggest why?

◆ Investigate how to keep an ice cube cold. Use the same packaging as used with the hot potatoes. Do they get the same results? Does an insulator keep cold things cold and warm things warm?

◆ Ask the children to bring in a collection of winter and summer clothing. Ask them to look at the differences in the fabrics. What is it about the winter fabrics that helps us keep warm? Why do they think the summer fabrics help us keep cool? Can they set up an investigation to see if they are right?

Our jacket potato reports

1

We tested different food packaging to see which one kept a potato hot. It was the tin foil freezer carton. I didn't think it would be because a freezer carton keeps things cold.

2

We wanted to find out which fast food packaging kept a potato hot best so we all thought about which packaging to use. Some people said bubble wrap and hay but you don't get food delivered in those! I chose a polystyrene carton like the ones you get burgers in because I've got some at home from when Uncle Jim took us for a burger after the pictures. Callum said he chose polystyrene but I chose it first! We had to cook the potatoes first so Mrs Long did it for us, then she told us to put one potato in each packaging. We left the potatoes for a few minutes (we had already taken their temperature with a thermometer). And then after 15 minutes we took it again. We decided how long to wait before we began the experiment. I chose 15 minutes because that's how long it takes me to get home from the fish and chip shop. Mrs Long said it was a sensible time so everyone did 15 minutes. At the end we took the temperature with a thermometer again to see which one was warmest. It wasn't the polystyrene carton which surprised me because I thought it would be.

3

What we wanted to find out:

We wanted to find out which fast food packaging is best to keep a jacket potato hot.

What we did:

1. Mrs Long cooked the potatoes.

2. We recorded their temperatures using a thermometer.

3. We wrapped each potato in a different container: polystyrene carton, a tin-foil freezer carton, a cardboard box and white paper.

4. The potatoes were left for 15 minutes.

5. After 15 minutes we recorded their temperatures again. The difference between the start and finish temperature was recorded for each piece of packaging.

What we found out:

We found out that the packaging with the smallest difference in temperature was the most successful at keeping the jacket potato warm. The tin foil freezer carton showed the smallest difference.

Literacy through science
KS2 Y3–4/P4–5

Photocopiable
©Hopscotch Educational Publishing

✦ Keeping warm ✦

✦ Below is a science report written by Rebekah. She has included lots of things that are not important to the report. Read it through carefully and cross out anything you think is not needed.

It was nearly Christmas and our class was talking about presents. I said I wanted a hot water bottle cover made to look like a rabbit. Aaron said that he wanted one that looked like a rhinoceros. Well anyone knows that you wouldn't want a rhino in your bed at night, they're not even furry. And I said that the bottle would probably burn him through the fabric. Anyway Mrs Long said that we should investigate which material is best for a hot water bottle cover.

Aaron said it depended on what you mean by best so we decided that it was the one that kept the bottle warmest for longest. We filled up little plastic bottles that Mrs Long got with quite hot water. We didn't use boiling water because it might be dangerous. We took the temperature every 10 minutes. Before we started we decided to test fur fabric, some blanket, bubble wrap, felt and cotton.

We wrapped each bottle in a sample of each material but we took the temperature of the water at the beginning. I had to help Sarita because she couldn't read the thermometer very well because she had left her glasses at home. We took the temperature every 10 minutes until the end of the lesson. The best material was the one with the highest temperature of water. It was the bubble wrap that Mita chose. I think it was a silly material for a hot water bottle cover!

✦ Now re-write the report by completing the following sentences.

We decided to find out which material is best to make a hot water bottle cover.

We used the following materials: _____

_____

We wrapped the materials around _____ filled with _____

_____

We took the temperature of the water every _____

The best material was the one with _____

The best material was_____

Keeping warm

✦ Read Rebekah's science report below. Cross out
  anything you think is not needed. Then complete
  the report using the headings provided.

It was nearly Christmas and our class was talking about presents. I said I wanted a
hot water bottle cover made to look like a rabbit. Aaron said that he wanted one
that looked like a rhinoceros. Well anyone knows that you wouldn't want a rhino in
your bed at night, they're not even furry. And I said that the bottle would probably
burn him through the fabric. Anyway Mrs Long said that we should investigate
which material is best for a hot water bottle cover.

Aaron said it depended on what you mean by best so we decided that it was the
one that kept the bottle warmest for longest. We filled up little plastic bottles that
Mrs Long got with quite hot water. We didn't use boiling water because it might be
dangerous. We took the temperature every 10 minutes. Before we started we
decided to test fur fabric, some blanket, bubble wrap, felt and cotton.

We wrapped each bottle in a sample of each material but we took the temperature
of the water at the beginning. I had to help Sarita because she couldn't read the
thermometer very well because she had left her glasses at home. We took the
temperature every 10 minutes until the end of the lesson. The best material was the
one with the highest temperature of water. It was the bubble wrap that Mita chose.
I think it was a silly material for a hot water bottle cover!

What we wanted to find out:

What we did:

1. We selected 5 materials to test: fur fabric, blanket, bubble wrap, felt and
   cotton.

2.

3.

4.

What we found out:

Activity 3

Name _____

✦ Keeping warm ✦

✦ Below is a science report written by Rebekah.
Select the most important information then rewrite
it, setting it out in a clear, well ordered way.

It was nearly Christmas and our class was talking about presents. I said I wanted a
hot water bottle cover made to look like a rabbit. Aaron said that he wanted one
that looked like a rhinoceros. Well anyone knows that you wouldn't want a rhino in
your bed at night, they're not even furry. And I said that the bottle would probably
burn him through the fabric. Anyway Mrs Long said that we should investigate
which material is best for a hot water bottle cover.

Aaron said it depended on what you mean by best so we decided that it was the
one that kept the bottle warmest for longest. We filled up little plastic bottles that
Mrs Long got with quite hot water. We didn't use boiling water because it might
be dangerous. We took the temperature every 10 minutes. Before we started we
decided to test fur fabric, some blanket, bubble wrap, felt and cotton.

We wrapped each bottle in a sample of each material but we took the temperature
of the water at the beginning. I had to help Sarita because she couldn't read the
thermometer very well because she had left her glasses at home. We took the
temperature every 10 minutes until the end of the lesson. The best material was
the one with the highest temperature of water. It was the bubble wrap that Mita
chose. I think it was a silly material for a hot water bottle cover!

✦ Write Rebekah's improved report here:

Solids and liquids

 Literacy objectives

+ To evaluate advertisements for interest, impact, appeal and honesty.
+ To design own advertisement or poster.

Science objectives

+ To know that some things can exist as both a solid and a liquid.
+ To know that a solid can be changed into a liquid by heating and this is called melting.

Resources

+ A selection of advertisements from magazines or television.

Starting point: Whole class

+ Tell the children that they are going to look at some advertisements today. Where are advertisements used? What kinds of things are advertised? Why?
+ Show them the selection of advertisements. Which ones do they think are best? Why? Is it the pictures or the words used or both? What attracts them so much to these advertisements? Do they use a famous personality or something that appeals to them? Would they persuade them to buy the product? Why/Why not?
+ Next tell them they are going to look at three advertisements that advertise the same product. Explain that you want them to think about the differences between them.

 Using the photocopiable text

+ Enlarge the texts on page 48 on a photocopier or arrange for each pair of children to have a copy. Read the three texts. What are they advertising? In what ways are they different from one another? Who are they aimed at? Which one is aimed at children? Adults? Both? Which one do you think is most convincing? Why?
+ Discuss the language used in each of the three texts. Are there any exaggerated claims made? Are some words used to grab attention? Does any of the language used help people remember the advertisment? (Rhyme, alliteration.)
+ Discuss the honesty of the advertments. How does text 1 differ from the others? Is honesty something that is common in advertisements? Why/why not? Do we believe everything we see/read in them?
+ How could each of the advertisements be improved? What could be added to text 3, for example? (Music?) These advertisements are presented in black and white. How effective is this? How important a role does colour have in an advertisement? Why?
+ Tell the children that you want them to design their own advertisement, taking into consideration all the things they have just discussed.

Group activities

Using the differentiated activity sheets

Activity sheet 1: This is aimed at children who would find it difficult to write their own advertising slogans. They are required to add appropriate illustrations and words to enhance a jingle.

Activity sheet 2: This is aimed at children who are beginning to consider the use of language in advertisements. They are asked to use the same words in an advertisement but in a different way.

Activity sheet 3: This is aimed at more able children who are capable of writing persuasive advertising slogans. They are required to improve a text.

Solids and liquids

 Plenary session

◆ Share the advertising posters. How effective do they consider them to be? Have they used persuasive wording? Bright, bold lettering? Appropriate pictures? How are the posters set out? Are they simple? Too cluttered? Is the writing clear and easy to read? What draws a person's attention to the poster? How could they be improved?

◆ Look again at some of the sample advertisements from magazines. How do the children's posters compare? What techniques have they used that are in these advertisements? Do they think the Tidy Taste company would be pleased with their work?

◆ Follow up ideas for literacy

◆ Ask the children to invent a new product of their own. They could design a whole advertising campaign to launch the product – radio jingles, television advertisements, magazine advertisments, billboard posters and so on. Encourage them to continually evaluate their designs and the type of language used to convince and persuade.
◆ Ask the children to video their favourite television advertisment. Share a selection of them. Ask each person to justify their choice.

◆ As a creative writing stimulus, ask each child to hold a chocolate button in the hand they do not write with. As the button melts, ask the children to write down a description of what is happening!!!!!
◆ Read stories and poems about chocolate. Ask the children to write their own poems.
◆ Make a collection of food/sweet wrappers. Discuss the language used to attract attention/inform. Ask the children to design their own wrappers.

Follow up ideas for science

◆ Investigate melting and dissolving to ensure the children understand the difference in terms.
◆ Give them a range of everyday substances and let them investigate which will dissolve and which won't. Is there another state that appears to be in between? Introduce suspension.
◆ Investigate whether all things that melt return to their former state on cooling.
◆ Ask the children to find ways of preventing things from melting. Ask them to record what they did and what happened. Can they suggest why they obtained the results they did?

◆ Ask them to use information books and/or CD-Roms to find out about things that have to be heated before they melt, such as molten metals. Ask them to describe what has to be done to a metal to make it melt. Why do they have to be melted in the first place?
◆ Ask the children to find out how chocolate is made. Ask them to draw a flow diagram of the chocolate-making process.
◆ Carry out a sensory investigation! Can the children identify different flavoured chocolates from taste/smell/sight or touch alone? Ask them to record the results in a chart or table. (Be aware of dietary allergies.)

1

Tidy Taste

Our NEW chocolate bar is GUARANTEED NOT TO MELT in normal weather conditions or when held in the hand. It will soften slightly but will not make a mess of your clothes or hands.

If your new **TIDY TASTE** bar does make a mess when held in your hand, we will REFUND YOUR MONEY!!

2

Tidy Taste

TIDY TASTE - the NEW NON-MELT chocolate bar that all MUMS have been waiting for!!
No more messy fingers!

No more messy clothes!

NEW **Tidy Taste** will NOT melt in your hand and leaves your child clean and tidy and wanting more!!!!

3

Tidy Taste

Want all the taste and no mess?

Try **Tidy Taste**...

In your lunch box
On the bus
At the office
There's no fuss
All dressed up and off to town
Tidy Taste won't let you down!

Literacy through science
KS2 Y3–4/P4–5

Photocopiable
©Hopscotch Educational Publishing

My advertisement

◆ Use the space around the wording of the *Tidy Taste* jingle to make an advertising poster. Add pictures and writing to make it more effective. Colour it in.

Want all the taste and no mess?

Try *Tidy Taste*...

　　In your lunch box
　　On the bus
　　At the office
　　There's no fuss
　　All dressed up and off to town
　　Tidy Taste won't let you down!

My advertisement

◆ You are going to design your own *Tidy Taste* advertisement. Read the words used in this advertisement again. Then use some of the same words and phrases to design your own advertisement. Make it more interesting and exciting.
Colour it in.

TIDY TASTE – the NEW NON-MELT chocolate bar that all MUMS have been waiting for!!

No more messy fingers!

No more messy clothes!

NEW *Tidy Taste* will NOT melt in your hand and leaves your child clean and tidy and wanting more!!!!

My advertisement

♦ You are going to re-write and improve this *Tidy Taste* advertisement. Make it sound more persuasive but still truthful! Use more interesting and exciting words. Make the poster bright and colourful.

> Our NEW chocolate bar is GUARANTEED NOT TO MELT in normal weather conditions or when held in the hand. It will soften slightly but will not make a mess of your clothes or hands.
>
> If your new **TIDY TASTE** bar does make a mess when held in your hand, we will REFUND YOUR MONEY!!

Friction

Literacy objectives

✦ To identify the main points of a text.
✦ To make notes.
✦ To write a newspaper style report.

Science objectives

✦ To know that the force between two moving surfaces in contact is called friction.
✦ To know that friction can be useful.

✦ Resources

✦ A collection of newspaper front pages.

✦ Starting point: Whole class

✦ Tell the children that they are going to look at some newspaper articles. Show some of the front pages. Look at the style and layout – how the headlines, text and photographs are set out.
✦ Talk about the way a newspaper article often begins with a synopsis of the story followed by a more detailed account, including quotes from eye witnesses or interviews when appropriate.
✦ Share some of the stories. Discuss the 'newspaper' style of writing. Is it like a storybook, information book or a report? Does the writer use any special techniques to draw us into the story – sensational headlines or opening comments, for example.
✦ Explain that they are now going to read an interview with an old lady who witnessed an accident and then they are going to write a newspaper report about it.

✦ Using the photocopiable text

✦ Enlarge the text on page 54 on a photocopier or arrange for each pair of children to have a copy. Share the text with them.
✦ What is the purpose of the text? (A police statement.) Will the policeman need to change this statement before it goes to court? Are all the details that Mrs Jenkins provides necessary to the report? Why/why not?
✦ Go through the beginning of the text, sentence by sentence and discuss what is important and what can be left out. Underline the important facts.
✦ Now model how these underlined facts can be written down as notes and then changed into a report. For example, 'Mrs Jenkins', 'Tuesday', 'Bridge Street crossing', 'busy traffic', 'very cold day' and 'icy and slippery' could be written as: 'On Tuesday Mrs Jenkins was standing at the busy Bridge Street crossing. It was a very cold day and the roads and pavements were very icy and slippery.'
✦ Explain that this is how a newspaper reporter would prepare her report – by using her notes to write up the sentences. Tell them that sometimes she might also use a story board, which is like a cartoon strip, to tell the main points of a story in pictures. Show the example from Activity sheet 1 to illustrate this.
✦ Tell the children that they are now going to write up a newspaper report based on Mrs Jenkins' statement.

Group activities

Using the differentiated activity sheets

Activity sheet 1: This is aimed at children who need help in identifying the main points in a story and in writing a newspaper report.

Activity sheet 2: This is aimed at children who can use a list of main points to write a report.

Activity sheet 3: This is aimed at more able children who can select the main ideas for note-making and use their own notes to write a report.

Friction

 Plenary session

- Share some of the children's reports. How accurate were they to the original statement? Have they changed anything? Did they include all the main points/facts? How useful was it to have a story board or notes? Does this make it easier to write the sentences? What headlines did the children in Group 3 invent? Which one has the greatest impact? Why?

- Refer back to the newspaper front page samples. Are the children's reports written in a similar style? How difficult/easy is it to write in this style? How does it compare with writing an invented story, for example? What things did they use to help them? (Mrs Jenkins' statement text, dictionary, thesaurus.) Can they see where they might improve their report?

 Follow up ideas for literacy

- Use the notes to write a different report – one that the policeman might write for a court hearing or police record file.
- Ask the children to write an account from the milkman's point of view! How might he have felt? How close did he come to death?
- Explore newspaper headlines. Discuss the use of bold typeface and capitals. Explore the sensationalism of headlines and how they are designed to tempt people to buy the paper.

Encourage the children to write their own headlines.
- Use ICT to write newspaper reports so that the children learn to lay out pages as well as edit reports to fit a particular space.
- Set up your own classroom newspaper. Advertise certain jobs and invite the children to apply for them. Hold interviews. Challenge the editor to organise a reporting team. Appoint a productions manager to oversee the layouts and printing.

 Follow up ideas for science

- Discuss why the cars could not stop on the icy road. Discuss how friction can help us in everyday lives. Ask the children to write two lists – where high friction is helpful (car tyres, shoe soles) and where low friction is useful (ice-skating, ten-pin bowling).
- Discuss how some steep roads have 'run-off' lanes in case brakes fail. Ask the children to investigate the best surface to stop a toy car.
- Explore sliding further. Ask them to investigate on which surfaces things slide most easily. Can they suggest why?
- Visit a tyre company. Find out what kind of tread is designed for particular road surfaces.

Relate this to shoe soles. Investigate which trainer sole has the best grip. Suspend from the trainer a container on a length of string. Add weights to the container until the trainer is pulled off the table. Repeat on a greasy table surface. What effect does this have?
- Challenge the children to make the fastest marble run! Line the marble run with different textured surfaces or make the run out of different materials to find the one with lowest friction. Ask them to record their results in some way – tables, charts. Provide stop watches.

"I was on my way to town. I always go on a Tuesday because my pension is due and I pop into the market to buy a nice piece of fish for tea. Anyway, I was at the crossing on Bridge Street. It's very busy there now since they opened that new industrial estate. The traffic was dreadful and of course the weather made it worse.

It was a very cold day. It had frozen hard in the night and the pavements were very icy and slippery. I expect the roads were too as most of the cars were going really slowly. Of course – there's always one or two in a hurry isn't there and this morning there were these two cars just charging along towards the industrial estate.

Well, the milk float was having trouble getting across Bridge Street on the slippery surface and about half way over it got stuck. Its wheels were spinning round, it just couldn't get a grip. Both these cars I was telling you about saw it there, but like I said they were going too fast. When they put their brakes on, they both started sliding towards the milk float.

I could see there was going to be a crash and so could the milkman because he jumped off the float and slid quickly across the road! Well, the first car, a red one, hit the float with a horrible bang, and the second car, a blue one, ran into the back of the first! The drivers got out, thankfully they both looked unhurt, but then they both started shouting at each other about bad brakes but I'm not sure good brakes would have helped. What do you think, Constable?"

Activity 1

✦ Newspaper report ✦

✦ Below is a story board showing the main parts of Mrs Jenkins' statement. Decide what you would draw in the last two boxes. Re-read the text very carefully to help you decide. Draw and colour the pictures.

✦ Now use the story board to complete the newspaper article below:

The Smithtown Gazette	Wednesday 16th February 2000

MILK FLOAT DISASTER!

Severe icy road conditions cause another serious crash in town.

Yesterday morning Mrs Sarah Jenkins was a witness to the crash involving a milk float and _____.
This is her account: "...there were these two _____ just charging along towards the _____. Well, the _____ was having trouble getting across _____ St ...

...and it got stuck...the first car hit the _____ with a horrible bang and the second ran into the back of the _____ _____."
Luckily, no-one was hurt but the milk float was _____.

Photocopiable

Newspaper report

✦ Use the notes in the box to help you complete the newspaper report below. Make sure you include all the facts.

Tuesday, Bridge Street crossing	Mrs Jenkins – eye-witness
weather very cold – roads icy	two cars travelling too fast
milk float gets stuck in middle of road	milkman gets out of float
red car hits float, blue car hits red car	no-one hurt, milk float damaged

The Smithtown Gazette	Wednesday 16th February 2000
MILK FLOAT DISASTER! Severe icy road conditions cause another serious crash in town. Yesterday morning	

©Hopscotch Educational Publishing

✦ Newspaper report ✦

✦ Use the text about Mrs Jenkins' statement to make notes about the facts concerning the traffic accident. Write your notes here.

```

```

✦ Now use your notes to write a newspaper report about it. Invent an eye-catching headline. Make sure you include all the facts and some quotes from Mrs Jenkins' statement as an eye-witness.

The Smithtown Gazette	Wednesday 16th February 2000

Chapter 10

Circuits and conductors

 Literacy objectives

✦ To notice and investigate devices for presenting texts, for example speech bubbles, enlarged or italicised print, captions, headings and inset text.
✦ To collect information from a variety of sources and present it in one simple format.

 Science objectives

✦ To understand that mains electricity can be dangerous.

 Resources

✦ Some information books/ CD-Roms about electricity that includes information about safety issues.

 Starting point: Whole class

✦ Ask the children what they know about electricity. What kinds of things run on mains electricity? What kinds of things run on small batteries? What is the difference between mains electricity and the electricity in small batteries? Which one is safer to use? Why?
✦ Are there any rules that they know of to do with safety when using mains electricity? List their ideas on the board.
✦ Tell the children that they are now going to read a cartoon about the hazards of mains electricity and how to prevent accidents. Explain that when they are looking at the cartoon you want them to look for two things:
1   How many safety ideas are mentioned.
2   How many different ways the cartoon uses to get the ideas across.

 Using the photocopiable text

✦ Enlarge the text on page 60 on a photocopier or arrange for each pair of children to have a copy. Share the cartoon together. Read the captions and

discuss the safety issues mentioned in the cartoon. Add any new ones to the list already on the board.
✦ Then discuss the different devices used for presenting the ideas. Begin with the speech bubbles. Can the children tell you which ones are speech bubbles and which ones are thought bubbles? Why do they think the cartoonist has used both kinds? Why do they think some words are in bold or italicised print? How does this help us to read the text? Why are so few words used in the cartoon? Discuss how the text has to be brief and concise to get the message across.
✦ How important are the illustrations? Do they tell us things without the need of words?
✦ What other device is used to get a message across? (a poster) How effective are posters? In what ways are they similar to or different from cartoons?
✦ Finally, evaluate the cartoon itself. How effective do they think it is in getting a message across? Who do they think the cartoon is aimed at? Why do they think a cartoon was used rather than some other way of presenting the ideas?
✦ Show the children the collection of information books about electricity. Find some pages that give information about safety issues. Look at the different ways that the ideas are presented – as a list, perhaps, as a block of text, a chart or a labelled diagram. Compare the cartoon method of getting information across with these other ideas. Which one do they think is most effective? Why? Explain that you want them to use all the ideas they can find about the safe use of electricity – their own knowledge, the list on the board, the cartoon strip and information from books – to create their own cartoon strip.

 Group activities

Using the differentiated activity sheets

Activity sheet 1: This is aimed at children who need support in setting out a cartoon and in deciding what safety issues to present.

Circuits and conductors

Activity sheet 2: This is aimed at children who have some experience of drawing cartoons and are able to find out further information about electrical safety issues.

Activity sheet 3: This is aimed at children who are experienced at collecting information from a variety of sources and can present their ideas succinctly in a cartoon format.

 Plenary session

✦ Share some of the children's cartoons. Did they remember to use capitals, bold or italicised print to emphasise a point? Did they use thought and speech bubbles? What other safety issues did they come up with? Are they happy with their cartoons? Do they get their message across clearly and succinctly? Could they be improved in any way?

 Follow up ideas for literacy

✦ Collect other examples of different types of cartoons (including political ones). What similarities do they have? What techniques do they use to get their message across? How many of them are humorous? Is cartoon humour different from other types of humour? In what ways?

✦ Ask the children to use information books/ CD-Roms to find out more information about electricity. They could draw and label a flow diagram showing how it reaches our homes, for example.

✦ Ask the children to use the information they have learned about safety with mains electricity to design posters warning people about electrical safety in the school. Display the posters in relevant places.

✦ Compare the way speech is set out in story books with cartoons. Revise how speech is set out. Ask the children to re-write the cartoon as a story that incorporates speech.

 Follow up ideas for science

✦ Carry out an investigation to find out which types of materials are electrical insulators. Discuss the need for insulators. What else can we insulate against apart from electricity? (Heat – oven gloves, cold – woolly hat and so on.) Provide a circuit wired up with a switch and a bulb. Ask the children to connect the circuit and explain why the bulb lights up. Challenge them to make a break in the circuit and attach different materials one at a time to record what happens. Then ask them to tell you which materials would make good electrical insulators and why. Ask them to consider other factors that are also important, such as flexibility and waterproofing.

✦ Ask the children to prove that metals are good conductors of electricity. Provide them with a wide variety of different metals.

✦ Challenge them to make their own simple switches in an electrical circuit. Provide them with paper clips, card and paper fasteners. Ask them to tell you why they think switches are important. What is their purpose?

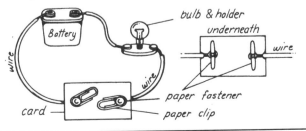

Activity 1

◆ Sam Spark ◆

◆ You are going to complete another cartoon strip about Sam Spark.

  Remember the following:

  1. Keep the sentences short and to the point.

  2. Use capitals, bold or italicised print when necessary

Activity 2   **Name** _____

✦ Sam Spark ✦

✦ You are going to complete another cartoon strip
about Sam Spark. Write the speech for the first three
squares. Then use information books to find three
other safety issues about electricity. Draw Sam Spark
telling people in his family about these three things in
the last three squares of the cartoon strip.

Sam Spark has some more good advice for you. Make sure you read what he says…		
Oh no, Sara, NEVER play with these.		

Literacy through science
KS2 Y3–4/P4–5

Photocopiable

◆ Sam Spark ◆

◆ You are going to draw another cartoon strip about Sam Spark. Use your own knowledge and information books to find more safety issues about electricity. One idea is done for you. Write in the speech bubble what Sam might be saying. Then draw Sam telling different people in his family about five other things.

Sam Spark has some more good advice for you. Make sure you read what he says…